PORTALS TO READING

Reading Skills Through Literature

SOUNDER

William H. Armstrong

Reproducible Activity Book
by
Claudia Dutcher Tillman

A Note from the Author

The activities in this workbook will introduce students to the time-tested literature that should be an important part of the reading program in every school. The activities will provide students from grades four through eight with meaningful reading experiences and, at the same time, reinforce a wide variety of reading skills.

Clearly, such literary matters as style and flavor may be experienced only by reading the primary source—the book itself. So, obviously, reading the book is the student's first responsibility. Students should be reminded frequently that the workbook activities are no substitute for the original text.

Rather, the workbook activities have been designed to encourage the student to read the original text—that is, the actual words of the author. These motivating workbook activities are often based on sentences and paragraphs especially written to support the teaching objective of each workbook lesson. Thus, I have declined to tinker with the words of the author and leave them properly where they belong—in their pure form in the pages of the novel.

—Claudia Dutcher Tillman

Table of Contents

Word Attack Skills

Comprehension Skills

Study Skills

Creative Skills

Author! Author!

WILLIAM H. ARMSTRONG

William H. Armstrong was born on a farm in the Shenandoah Valley near Lexington, Virginia, on September 14, 1914.

Armstrong attended Augusta Military Academy. He graduated from Hampden-Sydney College in 1936 and later attended the University of Virginia. In 1945, Armstrong taught history at Kent School in Kent, Connecticut.

Armstrong wrote *Through Troubled Waters* in 1957. In 1963, he received the National School Bell Award from the National Association of School Administrators. Armstrong won the John Newbery Medal and the Lewis Carroll Shelf Award for *Sounder.*

Other books by Armstrong include *Barefoot in the Grass* and *Sour Land.*

The Story in Brief

The setting for *Sounder* is many years ago in a rural part of the southern United States. The main characters are a boy, his mother and father, and their hound, Sounder.

The boy and his family live a poor, lonely life as sharecroppers. The family often goes hungry because the weather has been bad for hunting.

One day, the father brings home a ham to his family. Soon afterwards, the father is accused of theft. When the sheriff takes the father away, Sounder runs after the wagon. A deputy shoots the dog, and he crawls away to die.

The boy is heartbroken after Sounder is shot. He searches for Sounder, hoping the dog is still alive. After two months, the dog returns home, but he is lame and has lost an eye.

Later, the family learns that the father is working with other convicts on a road gang. The boy decides to find his father. He sets off on several fruitless journeys.

While on one such trip, an old schoolteacher befriends the boy. The teacher realizes the boy is eager to learn to read. The teacher suggests that the boy stay and do chores in exchange for an education. Each summer the boy could return home to work in the fields. The boy and his mother agree to the plan.

After several years, the boy's father returns home. He has been severely crippled by a dynamite explosion in a prison quarry. Sounder greets his master with the rolling bark which had been missing during his master's absence.

One day after hunting season comes, the father and Sounder hobble off into the woods. The next day, the boy finds his father dead in the woods. Within a few weeks, Sounder also dies.

With his teacher's help, the boy realizes that the power and beauty of his father and Sounder live on, even though they have died.

Name ______________________

Changing Short Vowels

Read each sentence. Then look at the word that comes after each sentence. Change the vowel in the word to form a new word that will make sense in the sentence. Write the new word on the blank in the sentence.

Example: Sounder was just a ___pup___ when the boy's father found him. pop

1. The boy ________________ his fingers over the dog's head. run
2. The boy liked to lay ________________ hand on Sounder's coat. has
3. The father let the boy ________________ with Sounder. hint
4. He looked beyond the ________________ of light from the cabin. ram
5. The boy's father ________________ the porch. loft
6. They cracked the nuts on a ________________. rack
7. The ________________ rattled as Sounder licked it. pen
8. The mother picked walnut kernels with a ________________ hairpin. bunt
9. The ________________ body of the raccoon lay at the man's feet. lamp
10. The boy cracked walnut shells on a ________________ rock. flit
11. The mother sent the children to ________________. bud
12. The boy ate the crumbs from the ________________ basket. hall
13. The water in the ________________ boiled. pet
14. The boy had smelled ________________ only twice before. him
15. The stove glowed red in one or two ________________. spits

Supplying Long Vowels

One word in each of the following sentences is missing a vowel. Read each sentence. Put a vowel in each blank to form a word that will make sense in the sentence.

Example: The gr _e_ ase had soaked into the oak slab.

1. The October wind was very c ___ ld.
2. When the mother held a sick ch ___ ld, she hummed.
3. Every d ___ y, the children picked up walnuts.
4. Sounder would get to ___ at the ham-boilin'.
5. The school was eight m ___ les away.
6. The husks left a dark purple st ___ in.
7. Sounder's bark could be heard from one sl ___ pe to another.
8. The boy's father sharpened the kn ___ fe with the whetstone.
9. The boy walked down the old dusty r ___ ad.
10. The pants were patched with a pi ___ ce of striped material.
11. His father and Sounder always left together at n ___ ght.
12. Sometimes the mother t ___ ld stories.
13. The rocker squ ___ aked a bit as the woman rocked.
14. The wood shavings burned with a br ___ ght flame.
15. The woman began to f ___ ld up her apron.

Name ____________________

Making Compounds

Two words combined form a compound. Each word in Box A forms the first part of a compound. Each word in Box B forms the second part. In the blank in each sentence below, write the compound that best completes the sentence. Use a word from each box to make your compounds.

Box A	
country	over
clothes	~~share~~
door	whet
sow	window
bull	cotton
stove	

Box B	
side	belly
wood	dog
alls	pipe
~~croppers~~	stone
line	panes
way	

Example: The cabins of the *sharecroppers* were scattered far apart.

1. Sounder was part hound and part ________________.

2. Sounder's bark seemed to roll over the ________________.

3. The wind rattled the loose ________________.

4. Neighbors could stand in an open ________________ and hear Sounder.

5. Sounder started across the field and past the ________________ trees.

(continued)

Name ______________________

Making Compounds

Chapter One

6. The boy warmed himself by the glowing ____________ .

7. The woman patched the faded ____________ .

8. The man used a ____________ to sharpen his knife.

9. The father brought home lots of ____________ when he helped butcher the hogs.

10. The woman hung the sheets on the ____________ to dry.

Finding Base Words

Each word below has been formed by adding a suffix such as *ly*, *ed*, or *ing* to a base word. On the blank beside each word, write the base word.

Example: named *name*

1. shivering ________
2. sagged ________
3. motionless ________
4. louder ________
5. mellowness ________
6. suddenly ________
7. branches ________
8. bigger ________
9. noises ________
10. using ________
11. beginning ________
12. brownish ________
13. potatoes ________
14. powerful ________
15. closeness ________
16. dumplings ________
17. stories ________
18. continued ________
19. rising ________
20. humming ________

Name ______________________

Listening for Syllables

Say each of the words listed below to yourself. The number of vowel sounds you hear in each word will be the same as the number of syllables. Decide how many syllables are in each word. Then write the number on the blank after each word.

Example: passed __1__

1. whimpering ______
2. burlap ______
3. squeezed ______
4. whistle ______
5. wooden ______
6. yesterday ______
7. leaves ______
8. covering ______
9. combination ______
10. patched ______
11. woman ______
12. decided ______
13. younger ______
14. whole ______
15. together ______
16. smell ______
17. underneath ______
18. punctuated ______
19. remembered ______
20. cabin ______
21. worse ______
22. totally ______
23. anymore ______
24. empty ______
25. loneliness ______
26. coal ______
27. skillet ______
28. continued ______
29. separated ______
30. wedge ______

Name ______________________

Chapter Two

Classifying Word Groups

Read the following sentences. Decide if the italicized part of the sentence tells you *where*, *when*, or *how*. Underline the correct choice.

Example: The weeds grew *by the side of the road.* where when how

1. *In the summer*, the earth was soft. where when how
2. The boy stood *quietly* at the open door. where when how
3. The children sat *around the stove.* where when how
4. The boy went *quickly* into the cabin. where when how
5. The ground was frozen *during the winter.* where when how
6. Many people sat *on cabin porches.* where when how
7. People sometimes used the road *on a Saturday.* where when how
8. The white man spoke *loudly* to the family. where when how
9. A child had been sitting *on the stool.* where when how
10. The family needed wood *at night.* where when how

(continued)

Name ______________________

Classifying Word Groups

Chapter Two

11. Sounder sometimes stayed *under the porch.* where when how

12. The deputy spoke *roughly* to the boy's father. where when how

13. The mother talked *calmly* to her son. where when how

14. The boy looked *under the cabin.* where when how

15. *That night,* Sounder was wounded. where when how

16. The boy *carefully* set the lantern on the ground. where when how

17. The gravestones were nearly hidden *in the brambles.* where when how

18. The woman sat *in her rocking chair.* where when how

19. The boy *slowly* ate his supper. where when how

20. The boy hoped Sounder would return *by morning.* where when how

Classifying Words

In each group of words below, one word does not belong with the others. Draw a line through the word that does not belong.

Example: dust ~~patches~~ ground dirt

1. branch weeds track bush
2. wide land earth field
3. ham oak sausage pork
4. stool stove cloth table
5. room boy child man
6. growl whine swing bark
7. jaw tore leg foot
8. horse dog raccoon noise
9. scream holler raced yell
10. porch jacket overalls shirt
11. house hills cabin shed
12. pan kettle pot rocker
13. wind road clouds rain
14. speck lamp lantern light
15. summer winter cold autumn
16. oak pine cottonwood store
17. coat slab vest pants
18. dirty green brown black
19. hurt sore ache creep
20. trot run eat walk

Following Directions

Below is a drawing of a woods outside the family's cabin. Carefully read the paragraphs at the bottom of the page. Study the drawing, then locate each part underlined in the paragraphs. Write the name of each part on the correct blank.

The boy looked out the cabin window to the woods. The tallest tree he could see was a stately pine. He recognized the walnut tree with the twisted trunk which provided many walnuts for his mother. Next to the walnut was a cottonwood. Between the cottonwood and the pine stood a small poplar.

The flat stalk land, covered with broken brown stalks, was separated from the woods by a fencerow of crisscrossed rails. Next to the fencerow stood a large jack oak tree. Under the oak was a blackberry bush. Between the jack oak and the pine was a persimmon tree where Sounder sometimes treed raccoons.

1. ______________________
2. ______________________
3. ______________________
4. ______________________
5. ______________________
6. ______________________
7. ______________________
8. ______________________
9. ______________________

Name ______________________

Chapter Two

Remembering Details

The following questions are about some of the characters and events in the book. Write the answers on the lines after the questions. Be sure to use complete sentences.

1. What did the boy smell when he awoke? ______________________

2. Who came to the cabin? ______________________

3. What did one of the men put on the boy's father? ______________________

4. What did the man say the boy's father had taken? ______________________

5. Where did the men put the boy's father? ______________________

6. Who tried to hold on to Sounder? ______________________

7. What happened to Sounder when he got loose? ______________________

8. What did the boy find on the road? ______________________

Sequencing Events

The events listed below are arranged in incorrect sequence. Write *1* in the blank before the event that happened first, *2* before the event that happened next, and so on.

______ The boy watched his mother walk down the road.

______ The boy told the younger children he was going outside.

______ The boy walked down the road looking for Sounder.

______ The mother made biscuits and gravy for breakfast.

______ The boy could not find Sounder under the cabin.

______ The boy's mother said she was going to the store.

______ The boy took Sounder's ear out from under his pillow.

______ The mother wrapped the walnut kernels in a brown paper.

______ The boy crawled under the cabin to look for Sounder.

______ The boy took an armload of wood into the cabin.

Getting the Main Idea

Read each of the following paragraphs. Then read the four sentences below each paragraph. Choose the sentence that best states the main idea of the paragraph. Then neatly copy that sentence on the line provided.

a. The boy's mother wrapped the walnut kernels in brown paper and put the package into a basket. She hoped to sell the kernels at the store. Then she put on her brown sweater and tied a scarf over her head.

1. The boy liked to eat walnuts.
2. The mother prepared to go to the store.
3. The boy knew the air was cold.
4. The mother hummed as she walked.

____

b. The boy's mother told him to watch the fire while she was gone. She also told him not to leave the children alone with a roaring fire. The boy was supposed to warm some mush for dinner. The mother warned the boy not to speak to any strangers while she was gone.

1. The children would eat mush for dinner.
2. The mother was going to leave.
3. The mother told the boy what to do while she was away.
4. The mother would not eat supper at home.

____

(continued)

Name ______________________

Getting the Main Idea

Chapter Three

c. As the boy crawled under the cabin, he scraped his head and shoulders on nails. He cut his knees and elbows on bits of broken glass and rusty tin. Dust got in his mouth and cobwebs hung down in his face.

1. The boy had difficulty crawling under the cabin.
2. Sounder was not under the cabin.
3. The cabin was poorly built.
4. The cabin once stood on a garbage dump.

---

d. The boy searched for Sounder along the road. Then he circled the field, looking along the fencerows as he walked. He did not see Sounder under the cottonwoods or the jack oaks. The boy carefully picked his way through the Scotch-broom tangle, but Sounder was not there, either.

1. The boy felt lonely.
2. Sounder loved secluded places.
3. The boy walked until he was weary.
4. Sounder was not in the field or woods.

Determining Fact and Opinion

Some of the following sentences are statements of fact. Some are statements of opinion. In the blank before each sentence, write the letter *F* if that sentence is a statement of fact. Write *O* if that sentence is a statement of opinion.

Example: ___O___ Biscuits and gravy were good for breakfast.

________ 1. The smell of sausage was wonderful.

________ 2. The boy went outside and called for Sounder.

________ 3. The boy wore an old jacket of his father's.

________ 4. Old jackets cannot keep anyone warm.

________ 5. The mother wore a heavy sweater to the store.

________ 6. Patches on a sweater look silly.

________ 7. Walnut kernels are delicious to eat.

________ 8. Warmed mush makes a good dinner.

________ 9. The mother carried the ham in a meal sack.

________ 10. The mother hummed as she walked along.

(continued)

Name ____________________

Determining Fact and Opinion

Chapter Three

________ 11. The boy watched his mother walk down the road.

________ 12. Only fools talk to the moon or the sun.

________ 13. Crying is useless and childish.

________ 14. The boy put wood into the stove.

________ 15. Sheets should be washed every week.

________ 16. The boy took Sounder's ear out from under a pillow.

________ 17. Curtains feel soft and cool.

________ 18. The boy crawled under the cabin.

________ 19. Answering riddles is fun.

________ 20. Cobwebs hung under the cabin.

Name ______________________

SOUNDER

Chapter Three

Remembering Details

The following questions are about some of the characters and events in the book. Write the answers on the lines after the questions. Be sure to use complete sentences.

1. Why did the boy's mother make the boy wear old clothes? ______________________

____

2. Why was the boy's mother taking walnuts to the store? ______________________

____

3. What was the boy to do if a stranger came? ______________________

____

4. What did the boy's father speak to when he stood on the porch? ______________________

____

5. How did the boy think that people would treat his mother? ______________________

____

6. What did the boy's mother plan to buy at the store? ______________________

____

7. What chore did the boy's mother do for the people in the big houses? ______________________

____

8. What was Sounder's favorite spot? ______________________

____

Name ______________________

SOUNDER

Chapter Four

Drawing Conclusions

In each of the following paragraphs, an item is described but not named. Read each paragraph and decide what is being described. Write your answers on the blank after each question.

1. The boy hated it. It blew right through his clothing and made him shiver. It blew through the woods, and the woods became noisy. It also made a whistling sound in the stovepipe that bothered the boy.

   What made the boy shiver? ______________________

2. Every now and then, a gray one crossed in front of the sun. Then it cast a shadow over the cabin and the nearby fields. It darkened the windows as it passed.

   What crossed in front of the sun? ______________________

3. The boy's mother made one and then baked it in the oven. It smelled delicious. Then she took it out and covered the layers with icing. She gave the children the pans to lick.

   What did the mother make? ______________________

(continued)

Name ______________________

Drawing Conclusions

Chapter Four

4. The boy wished someone would give an old one to his mother. If she had one, maybe he could learn to read. He longed to open its hard covers and look through all its pages.

   What did the boy wish he had? ______________________

5. There was a huge one on the courthouse roof. When both its great hands reached twelve, it rang twelve times. It was so loud, it seemed to shake the whole town.

   What was on the courthouse roof? ______________________

6. A man opened a huge iron gate and pushed the boy inside. The boy walked down a hallway lined with iron bars. He stopped by the gate that his father stood behind. The boy was glad to see that his father's hands and feet were not chained.

   Where was the boy's father? ______________________

Name ____________________

Determining Cause and Effect

To determine a cause, ask "What is the reason?" To determine an effect, ask "What is the result?" Match the causes and effects below. Write the number of the cause in front of its effect.

Cause		Effect
1. The boy saw someone walking down the road.	_____	The storekeeper gave her an empty cardboard box.
2. The boy knew his mother would not bring any candy.	_____	The boy had to go to the jail.
3. The mother needed a box for the cake.	_____	The boy hesitated before he knelt on the frozen ground.
4. The mother wanted to pick some walnut kernels.	_____	The jailer broke the cake into pieces.
5. The boy's knees were sore.	_____	The boy felt cold.
6. The wind blew through the boy's clothes.	_____	The boy knew his mother was coming home.
7. The mother wanted to make a cake.	_____	The mother sent the boy outside to crack some nuts.
8. Women were not allowed inside the jail.	_____	The mother had bought some vanilla.
9. The boy wanted to learn to read.	_____	He told the other children not to ask for any.
10. The jailer thought the boy might have hidden a steel file.	_____	He wished someone would give his mother a book.

Discovering Meaning Through Context

Read the following sentences. Three meanings are given for each italicized word. Use the context of the sentence to figure out which meaning is correct. Circle the correct meaning.

Example: Sounder might have been *addled* by a head wound and lost his way.

hurt   frightened   (confused)

1. The boy's mother went to the store to *fetch* some potatoes.

   test   get   price

2. The boy's fear *increased* as he got closer to town.

   turned over   faded   became greater

3. The boy and his father *peddled* mistletoe and berries around town.

   sold   hung   gathered

4. The drunken old man *staggered* down the sidewalk.

   ran   wobbled   jumped

5. The wild bull made a *lunge* forward and choked himself.

   small step   half turn   sudden movement

(continued)

Name ______________________

Discovering Meaning Through Context

Chapter Four

6. The boy walked down the long *corridor* inside the jail.

   row　　hallway　　cafeteria

7. The boy did not want to *quiver* and show that he was nervous.

   shake　　stutter　　cry

8. The father did not want his wife to *grieve* for him.

   beg　　feel sad　　fight

9. The father did not talk much, and the quiet *spell* grew longer.

   time　　day　　prayer

10. The father could skin the *carcass* of a dead possum with one hand.

    den　　family　　body

Name ____________________

SOUNDER

Chapter Five

Understanding Special Meanings

Read the following sentences. Explain in your own words the meaning of the italicized word or group of words. Write your response on the line below each sentence.

Example: Sounder headed for the hills whenever *he was given his head.*

he was allowed to go where he wanted

1. The boy and his father *kept their eyes peeled* for the white berries.

____

2. Each step the boy took down the hall *sounded like a giant walking.*

____

3. The huge red-faced man had a *bull neck.*

____

4. *The quiet spell was split* by the clank of an iron door.

____

(continued)

Name ______________________

Understanding Special Meanings

Chapter Five

5. The boy's eyes *began to smart* from the dust and dirt.

____

6. The boy thought Sounder may have been *knocked senseless.*

____

7. Sounder would *speak to the moon in dog-talk.*

____

8. The mother walked down the road until she *became part of the road and earth.*

____

9. *The loneliness in the cabin pressed against* the boy, and his eyes and ears hurt.

____

10. The light from the lamp *ran outside* to the porch.

____

Name ____________________

SOUNDER

Chapter Five

Remembering Details

The following questions are about some of the characters and events in the book. Write the answers on the lines after the questions. Be sure to use complete sentences.

1. How did the boy describe the jailer to his mother? ____________________

____

2. What did the boy find on the porch? ____________________

____

3. What was wrong with the animal? ____________________

____

4. How far would Sounder go from the cabin? ____________________

____

5. What noise did Sounder no longer make? ____________________

____

6. What did the mother ask the people from the big houses to read to her? ______

____

7. What happened to the boy's father? ____________________

____

Remembering Details

To work the puzzle, use the words that complete the sentences below.

Across

2. The boy went to the ____ to see his father.
5. Sounder had lost part of one ____.
6. People from the big house read the ____ to the boy's mother.
9. The boy's father was sentenced to hard ____.
12. The ____ at the courthouse was mean.
14. The mother picked walnut ____.

Down

1. ____ was gone for many days.
2. The family lived in a ____.
3. The boy wished he could ____.
4. The boy heard a whine from the ____.
7. A possum ____ hung on the wall.
8. The father would send news by the visiting ____.
10. Sounder would no longer ____.
11. The jailer ruined the ____.
13. The boy's ____ had a straw tick.

Name ______________________

SOUNDER

Chapter Five

Matching Synonyms

A synonym is a word having the same or nearly the same meaning as another word. Choose a synonym for each word in the Word List. Write the synonym on the blank.

	Word List		Synonym
Example:	sick	ill	hop
1.	cry	______________	clean
2.	faster	______________	far
3.	jump	______________	print
4.	hound	______________	quicker
5.	pan	______________	difficult
6.	remote	______________	rip
7.	wide	______________	~~ill~~
8.	quiet	______________	broad
9.	wash	______________	pot
10.	hard	______________	quit
11.	excited	______________	hear
12.	stop	______________	weep
13.	write	______________	thrilled
14.	tear	______________	dog
15.	listen	______________	noiseless

Matching Antonyms

An antonym is a word which means the opposite or nearly the opposite of another word. Choose an antonym for each word in the Word List. Write the antonym on the blank.

	Word List		Antonym
Example:	back	*front*	remembered
1.	strength	______	closed
2.	few	______	lead
3.	afraid	______	scream
4.	forgotten	______	brave
5.	beautiful	______	farther
6.	follow	______	~~front~~
7.	darkness	______	noisy
8.	empty	______	ugly
9.	closer	______	began
10.	whisper	______	many
11.	warmed	______	full
12.	quiet	______	cooled
13.	smooth	______	weakness
14.	finished	______	wrinkled
15.	opened	______	light

Determining Alphabetical Order

Words are listed in a dictionary in alphabetical order. Number the six words in each list below to show the order in which they would appear in a dictionary. Write *1* on the blank before the word that comes first alphabetically, and so on.

Example:

3 big
1 barbed
4 brother
6 convict
5 chains
2 besides

A.

_____ soft
_____ singing
_____ spring
_____ stretch
_____ stamp
_____ speak

B.

_____ just
_____ known
_____ journey
_____ late
_____ knew
_____ line

C.

_____ waited
_____ yard
_____ wind
_____ would
_____ woods
_____ year

D.

_____ far
_____ dragging
_____ feet
_____ dressed
_____ enemy
_____ deep

E.

_____ ran
_____ people
_____ ringing
_____ papers
_____ post
_____ road

F.

_____ giant
_____ hear
_____ his
_____ great
_____ gate
_____ high

G.

_____ now
_____ many
_____ moved
_____ names
_____ months
_____ most

H.

_____ trees
_____ usually
_____ sneer
_____ uncle
_____ tired
_____ still

Name ______________________

Determining Alphabetical Order

Most of the words in the list below are in alphabetical order. However, some of the words have either jumped ahead or fallen back. Cross out the words that are too far ahead or too far back. The remaining words will then be in alphabetical order. Complete the Word-Search Puzzle by hunting down the correctly alphabetized words.

boy
clothesline
tracks
dreaming
edge
fields
uncle
gate
humming
state
jail
laugh
men
wages
mule
needles
night
easy
pine
railroads
hopeless
roar
tramping
chains
wind

Word-Search Puzzle

C A S D A O R L I A R B
L T D J P O F G C H Q I
O I L E A K G N I G H T
T M A R O H S I E R S G
H G N J G U E M Y N A N
E V A U F Z L A B T I I
S H A W I X D E E C N P
L L J E E M E R Q D X M
I K G L M L E D S R P A
N D U W U E N T O Y A R
E H U M M I N G Y Z O T
B D C V W S D L I E F B

Name ______________________

SOUNDER

Chapter Six

Using a Pronunciation Key

Use the key at the bottom of the page to help pronounce the respelled words. Write the word correctly spelled on the line beside the Respelled Word. Use the Word List to help figure out the Respelled Word.

Respelled Word		Word List
Example: (wuns)	once	prison
1. (jur′ nē)	______________	autumn
2. (koun′ tē)	______________	enemy
3. (i nuf′)	______________	county
4. (sə pōz′)	______________	afraid
5. (ôt′ əm)	______________	enough
6. (ri zem′ b'l)	______________	quarry
7. (krāt)	______________	lonely
8. (kwôr′ ē)	______________	resemble
9. (ə frād′)	______________	cedar
10. (prak′ tis)	______________	journey
11. (en′ ə mē)	______________	crate
12. (sē′ dər)	______________	practice
13. (priz′ 'n)	______________	~~once~~
14. (lōn′ lē)	______________	suppose

pat/ **cāke**/ **cär**/ **pet**/ **mē**/ **it**/ **nīce**/ **pot**/ **cōld**/ **nôrth**/
book/ **fo͞ol**/ **boil**/ **out**/ **cup**/ **mūle**/ **burn**/ **sing**/ **thin**/
*th*is/ hw in **wh**ite/ zh in plea**s**ure/ ə in **a**bout
The ′ mark indicates an accented syllable.

Name ______________________

SOUNDER

Chapter Six

Using Guide Words

At the top of each dictionary page are guide words. These words are the first and last words on a dictionary page. The other words on the page fall in alphabetical order between the guide words.

Put the boxed words below in alphabetical order under the correct guide words. One has been done for you.

stories	boy	frame
county	journey	numbers
guard	strangers	chase
man	mother	face
~~age~~	longer	reading
practice	easy	liked

act—fin	final—march	mare—tongue
1. age	1. ______	1. ______
2. ______	2. ______	2. ______
3. ______	3. ______	3. ______
4. ______	4. ______	4. ______
5. ______	5. ______	5. ______
6. ______	6. ______	6. ______

Name ____________________

Choosing Correct Meanings

The italicized word in each of the sentences below has several meanings. The meanings are listed in the Glossary. Decide which meaning the word has in the sentence. Then write the number of your choice on the blank.

Glossary

bark 1. outer covering of a tree 2. to scrape the skin off 3. sound that a dog makes 4. to speak sharply
blow 1. a hard hit 2. an unexpected event that causes unhappiness 3. to move with speed or force 4. to sound by a blast of air
lean 1. to stand at a slant 2. to rest on something for support 3. slim; trim 4. poor
look 1. see 2. to search 3. to appear or seem
mean 1. to have in mind 2. to be defined as 3. unkind 4. low quality
spot 1. a mark or stain 2. a place 3. to see or recognize

Example: __4__ "Get, boy! And get fast!" the guard *barked.*

_____ 1. A *lean* elderly man came from the schoolhouse.

_____ 2. There were several *spots* of blood on the boy's hand.

_____ 3. The boy wondered what the teacher could possibly *mean.*

_____ 4. The boy *looked* many places for his father.

_____ 5. The boy felt a sudden *blow* against his hand.

(continued)

Name ____________________

Choosing Correct Meanings

Chapter Seven

______ 6. The boy did not know what the words in the book could *mean.*

______ 7. The boy *leaned* against the fence post.

______ 8. Not finding his father was a *blow* to the boy.

______ 9. The years without the father was a *lean* time for the family.

______ 10. The dog began to *bark* at the schoolchildren.

______ 11. The guard seemed quite *mean.*

______ 12. The teacher's cabin was in a lovely *spot.*

______ 13. The wind began to *blow* the trees.

______ 14. The boy could easily *spot* danger.

______ 15. The boy *looked* at the teacher.

Name ______________________

Making an Outline

Read the article below. Think about the topics and subtopics of each paragraph. Use the Word List provided to outline the article. The topics should come after the numerals. The subtopics come after the capital letters. List the topics and subtopics in the order the items fall in the article.

Part of the outline has been done for you. Be sure to capitalize the first letter of the topics and subtopics.

Lamps

Lamps have been used for thousands of years to produce light. The earliest lamps were fat or oil lamps. One of the fuels used for this type of lamp is grease. Candles and fat lamps were made of tallow or paraffin. During the Middle Ages, whale oil was used. During the 1800s, the use of kerosene became widespread.

Gas lamps also produced light, but needed no wick. This type of lamp burned acetylene or natural gas. Other gases used in gas lamps included butane, coal gas, and water gas.

By the early 1900s, electric lamps had begun to replace other kinds of lamps. There are several types of electric lamps. The type found in most homes is the incandescent. Fluorescent lamps are used widely in offices and schools. Mercury vapor lamps stand along many highways. Metal halide lamps and neon lamps are also types of electric lamps.

(continued)

Name ____________________

Making an Outline

Chapter Seven

Lamps
____

I. Fat or oil
- A. ______________________
- B. ______________________
- C. ______________________
- D. ______________________
- E. ______________________

II. ______________________
- A. Acetylene
- B. ______________________
- C. ______________________
- D. ______________________
- E. ______________________

III. ______________________
- A. ______________________
- B. Fluorescent
- C. ______________________
- D. ______________________
- E. ______________________

Word List

Neon

~~Lamps~~

Paraffin

Gas

~~Acetylene~~

Metal halide

Whale oil

Electric

~~Fat or oil~~

~~Fluorescent~~

Kerosene

Coal gas

Butane

Water gas

Incandescent

Grease

Tallow

Natural gas

Mercury vapor

Name ______________________

Finding Facts in the Encyclopedia

A sample encyclopedia set is drawn below. Imagine that you need these volumes of the encyclopedia to respond to the questions below. Circle the word or words in each question that might help you find the answers.

Use the circled words to decide which volume or volumes you will need to answer each question. Write the volume number or numbers on the blank.

Example: ___17___ When were schools first set up in the United States?

__________ 1. What kind of stones are mined from a quarry?

__________ 2. What is a cistern?

__________ 3. Where can iron be found?

__________ 4. When were stoves first used?

__________ 5. What color is a weasel's fur?

__________ 6. Do most hounds have long tails?

__________ 7. When did printed books first appear?

__________ 8. How does a lantern provide light?

__________ 9. What did Michel Montaigne write?

__________ 10. What empire did Cyrus rule?

Name ______________________

Creating a Character

Imagine you are a young sharecropper living in a cabin in the South about the same time as the boy and his family. You are being interviewed by a newspaper reporter. Write your responses to the reporter's questions on the lines provided. Be sure to use complete sentences.

Reporter: Why is it important for your family to have a coon hound?

Sharecropper: ____

____

Reporter: What kind of chores do you do around the house?

Sharecropper: ____

____

Reporter: How do the townspeople treat you and your family?

Sharecropper: ____

____

Reporter: Do you ever become lonely in your cabin?

Sharecropper: ____

____

Reporter: Why is it important for you to go to school and learn to read?

Sharecropper: ____

____

Creating a Picture

Draw one of the scenes the author describes in Chapter Seven. Then write your own description of what you have drawn. Be sure to use complete sentences.

____

____

Name ______________________

Connecting Words

Look at the three words in each set below. Combine the words to form a sentence that expresses a complete thought. Write the sentence on the line after each group of words.

Example: book/read/learn *He wanted to learn to read the book.*

1. rocker/humming/porch ______________________
2. road/watch/far ______________________
3. dog/whining/jumping ______________________
4. yard/gate/fence ______________________
5. chores/cabin/teacher ______________________
6. fingers/bruised/bandaged ______________________
7. summer/fields/work ______________________
8. lantern/sack/wall ______________________
9. heat/drought/earth ______________________
10. master/limped/stiff ______________________
11. blast/pain/wounded ______________________
12. woodpile/kindling/fire ______________________
13. autumn/hunt/woods ______________________
14. trees/chop/timber ______________________
15. moon/shadows/night ______________________

Name ______________________

Writing a Journal Sample

Imagine that you are one of the characters in the book. In the sample journal below, describe one of these events from your character's viewpoint: the father's return, the father's death, or Sounder's death. Be sure to use complete sentences.

Character ______________________________________

Name ______________________

Using Descriptive Words

List seven words that can be used to describe each of the italicized words below. Be creative. Write your words on the blanks.

Example: *ghost*

1. pale
2. spooky
3. mischievous
4. floating
5. mysterious
6. shimmering
7. friendly

A. *dog*

1. ______
2. ______
3. ______
4. ______
5. ______
6. ______
7. ______

B. *cabin*

1. ______
2. ______
3. ______
4. ______
5. ______
6. ______
7. ______

C. *stories*

1. ______
2. ______
3. ______
4. ______
5. ______
6. ______
7. ______

D. *road*

1. ______
2. ______
3. ______
4. ______
5. ______
6. ______
7. ______

Name ______________________

Describing Feelings

A person does not always express feelings directly in words. Sometimes feelings are shown through other clues as well. Each of the sentences below provides clues to the feelings of a character in the book. The name of that character is italicized. First study the clues, then choose the word from the box that best describes the character's feelings. Write that word on the blank in front of the sentence.

sad	proud	lonely	ashamed	contented
angry	relieved	excited	amused	surprised

______________ 1. *The boy* was glad to sink his head into the sweet-smelling pillow and rest.

______________ 2. *The boy* chuckled at the sight of the dogs chasing the pig around the schoolhouse.

______________ 3. The sight of Sounder lying so still in the road brought tears to *the boy's* eyes.

______________ 4. *The boy* sighed gratefully when he saw finally saw his mother returning.

______________ 5. *The boy's* mouth dropped open when he saw not only the ham, but pork sausage as well.

______________ 6. There was nothing to do, no one to visit, and *the boy* felt empty inside.

______________ 7. *The boy* stood tall and felt warm inside when he saw his father hold the hot lid without using a rag.

______________ 8. *The guard* yelled fiercely at the boy, "Get out of here!"

______________ 9. *The boy* impatiently waited until the street was empty, and then he ran to fetch the book.

______________ 10. *The boy* hung his head and stared at his feet when the others teased him about his patched overalls.

Name ____________________

Explaining Feelings

The questions below ask you to describe the feelings you had as you read the book. Read each question carefully. Write your response on the lines provided. Explain why you felt the way you did. Be sure to use complete sentences.

1. How did you feel when the sheriff took the boy's father away?

____

____

____

2. How did you feel when the jailer broke the father's cake?

____

____

____

3. How did you feel when Sounder finally returned home?

____

____

____

(continued)

Name ________________

Explaining Feelings

4. How did you feel when the boy failed to find his father?

____

____

____

5. How did you feel when the teacher offered to educate the boy?

____

____

____

6. How did you feel when the boy's father returned home at last?

____

____

____

7. How did you feel when the boy's father died?

____

____

____

Optional Spelling and Vocabulary Lists

Below are six word lists from the book. The lists can be used as spelling or vocabulary words.

Chapter 1

shivering
harvest
possum
conversation
excited
muscles
neighbors
dumplings
whimper
biscuits
sausage
straightened
cabin
flour
search
coal
kernels
stain
burlap
kettle

Chapters 2—3

distinct
separate
evidence
curiosity
sprawled
kindling
potatoes
troublesome
curtains
squirrels
sorrow
distance
patches
metal
striped
thrust
lunge
gravy
breeze
crawl

Chapter 4

weaken
creatures
tomorrow
hesitated
sheriff
vanilla
mistletoe
increased
offered
staggered
hatred
corridor
poker
quiet
jail
fetch
afraid
jerked
burst
height

Chapters 5—6

grieved
cement
famished
lonesome
skeleton
direction
laundry
journey
autumn
familiar
recognize
terrifying
numb
empty
fret
prison
remote
weak
labor
crates

Chapter 7

crippled
silence
convicts
jagged
cruelty
building
commotion
usually
remember
answer
suddenly
exchange
search
fence
guard
midst
gaunt
instead
enroll
school

Chapter 8

bandaged
trouble
raccoons
finished
hobbled
considerate
anxious
hesitant
deserted
shoulder
awakened
branches
chores
creek
lilac
faint
stalk
whine
peace
echo

Supplementary Activities

Below is a list of ideas that could be used as supplementary or culminating activities.

I. Oral reading

A. To the entire class

B. To each other

C. To the teacher

D. To a tape recorder

II. Group discussions

A. Author's writing style

B. Ideas gained from the book

1. Most important

2. Most frightening

3. Most amusing

4. Most saddening

5. Most exciting

6. Most liked

D. Characters

1. Did the characters seem real?

2. What was the most admirable trait of each character?

3. What was the least admirable trait of each character?

4. Which character was the student's favorite? Why?

5. List questions to ask each character.

III. Spelling bee using words from the book

IV. Role play situations from the book

V. Artistic creations

A. Murals

B. Dioramas

C. Book jackets

D. Posters

E. Puppets

F. Poetry

G. Costumes

H. Portraits

I. Mobiles

J. Songs

K. Newspaper headlines, articles, and drawings

VI. Research

A. Sharecropping

B. Coon hound

C. Trees mentioned in the book

D. Wildlife mentioned in the book

VII. Read other books by the same author

Response Key

WORD ATTACK SKILLS

Changing Short Vowels (page 7)
1. ran; 2. his; 3. hunt; 4. rim; 5. left; 6. rock; 7. pan; 8. bent; 9. limp; 10. flat; 11. bed; 12. hull; 13. pot; 14. ham; 15. spots.

Supplying Long Vowels (page 8)
1. cold; 2. high; 3. day; 4. eat; 5. miles; 6. stain; 7. slope; 8. knife; 9. road; 10. piece; 11. night; 12. told; 13. squeaked; 14. bright; 15. fold.

Making Compounds (page 9)
1. bulldog; 2. countryside; 3. windowpanes; 4. doorway; 5. cottonwood; 6. stovepipe; 7. overalls; 8. whetstone; 9. sowbelly; 10. clothesline.

Finding Base Words (page 11)
1. shiver; 2. sag; 3. motion; 4. loud; 5. mellow; 6. sudden; 7. branch; 8. big; 9. noise; 10. froze; 11. begin; 12. brown; 13. potato; 14. power; 15. close; 16. dumpling; 17. story; 18. continue; 19. rise; 20. hum.

Listening for Syllables (page 12)
1. 3; 2. 2; 3. 1; 4. 2; 5. 2; 6. 3; 7. 1; 8. 3; 9. 4; 10. 1; 11. 2; 12. 3; 13. 2; 14. 1; 15. 3; 16. 1; 17. 3; 18. 4; 19. 3; 20. 2; 21. 1; 22. 3; 23. 3; 24. 2; 25. 3; 26. 1; 27. 2; 28. 3; 29. 4; 30. 1.

COMPREHENSION SKILLS

Classifying Word Groups (page 13)
1. when; 2. how; 3. where; 4. how; 5. when; 6. where; 7. when; 8. how; 9. where; 10. when; 11. where; 12. how; 13. how; 14. where; 15. when; 16. how; 17. where; 18. where; 19. how; 20. when.

Classifying Words (page 15)
1. track; 2. wide; 3. oak; 4. cloth; 5. room; 6. swing; 7. tore; 8. noise; 9. raced; 10. porch; 11. hills; 12. rocker; 13. road; 14. speck; 15. cold; 16. store; 17. slab; 18. dirty; 19. creep; 20. eat.

Following Directions (page 16)
1. walnut; 2. cottonwood; 3. poplar; 4. pine; 5. persimmon; 6. blackberry bush; 7. jack oak; 8. fencerow; 9. stalk land.

Remembering Details (page 17)
1. The boy smelled ham bone and pork sausage. 2. A sheriff and two deputies came to the cabin. 3. The man put handcuffs on the boy's father. 4. He said the boy's father took a ham from the smokehouse. 5. The men put the boy's father in a wagon. 6. The boy tried to hold Sounder. 7. The deputy shot Sounder. 8. The boy found part of Sounder's ear in the road.

Sequencing Events (page 18)
4, 7, 10, 1, 9, 3, 6, 2, 8, 5.

Getting the Main Idea (page 19)
a. The mother prepared to go to the store. b. The mother told the boy what he was to do while she was away. c. The boy had difficulty crawling under the cabin. d. Sounder was not in the field or woods.

Determining Fact and Opinion (page 21)
1. O; 2. F; 3. F; 4. O; 5. F; 6. O; 7. O; 8. O; 9. F; 10. F; 11. F; 12. O; 13. O; 14. F; 15. O; 16. F; 17. O; 18. F; 19. O; 20. F.

Remembering Details (page 23)
1. She knew the boy would be crawling under the cabin. 2. She was going to sell the walnuts. 3. The boy was not to say anything to a stranger. 4. The boy's father spoke to the wind, moon, and sun. 5. The boy thought people would be mean to his mother. 6. She planned to buy sowbelly and potatoes. 7. She washed sheets, pillowcases, and curtains for them. 8. Sounder's favorite spot was behind the porch steps.

Drawing Conclusions (page 25)
1. the wind; 2. a cloud; 3. a cake; 4. a book; 5. a clock; 6. in jail.

Determining Cause and Effect (page 27)
3, 8, 5, 10, 6, 1, 4, 7, 2, 9.

Discovering Meaning Through Context (page 29)
1. get; 2. became greater; 3. sold; 4. wobbled; 5. sudden movement; 6. hallway; 7. shake; 8. feel sad; 9. time; 10. body.

Understanding Special Meanings (page 31)
1. searched; 2. made a loud sound; 3. very thick; 4. the silence was broken; 5. began to hurt and water; 6. dazed; 7. howl at the moon; 8. faded into the distance; 9. the lonely silence in the cabin bothered; 10. the lamplight shone.

Remembering Details (page 33)
1. He told his mother that the jailer was mean. 2. Sounder was on the porch. 3. Sounder had lost one eye, part of one ear, and had hurt one leg. 4. Sounder would only go as far as the road. 5. Sounder would not bark. 6. She asked the people to read the court news to her. 7. He was sentenced to hard labor.

Remembering Details (page 34)

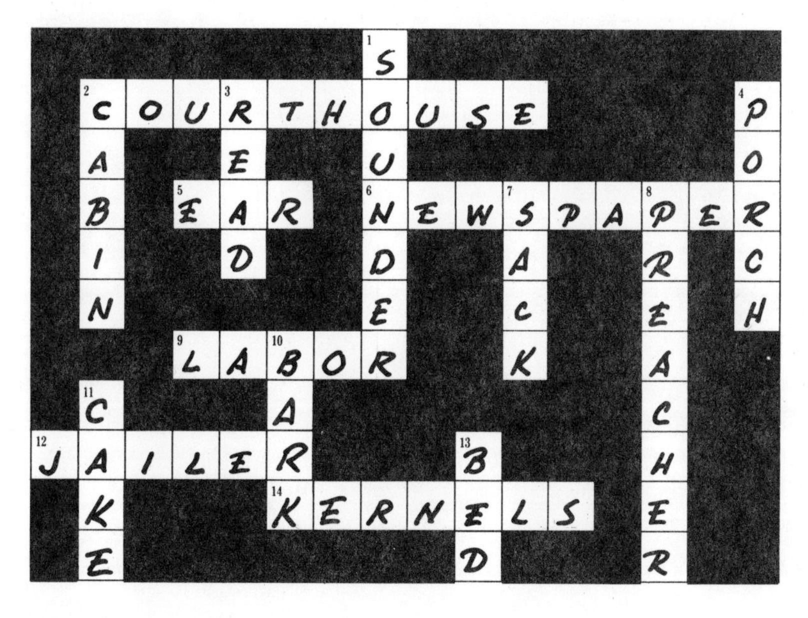

Matching Synonyms (page 35)
1. weep; 2. quicker; 3. hop; 4. dog; 5. pot; 6. far; 7. broad; 8. noiseless; 9. clean; 10. difficult; 11. thrilled; 12. quit; 13. print; 14. rip; 15. hear.

Matching Antonyms (page 36)
1. weakness; 2. many; 3. brave; 4. remembered; 5. ugly; 6. lead; 7. light; 8. full; 9. farther; 10. scream; 11. cooled; 12. noisy; 13. wrinkled; 14. began; 15. closed.

STUDY SKILLS

Determining Alphabetical Order (page 37)

A. 2, 1, 4, 6, 5, 3;
B. 2, 4, 1, 5, 3, 6;
C. 1, 5, 2, 4, 3, 6;
D. 5, 2, 6, 3, 4, 1;
E. 4, 2, 5, 1, 3, 6;
F. 2, 4, 6, 3, 1, 5;
G. 6, 1, 4, 5, 2, 3;
H. 4, 6, 1, 5, 3, 2.

Determining Alphabetical Order (page 38)

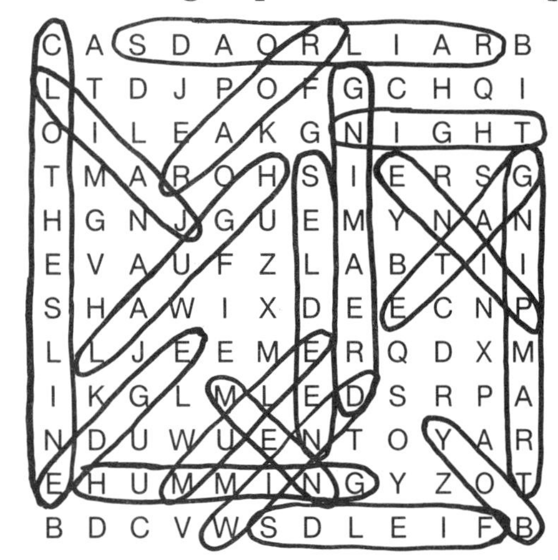

Words crossed out: tracks, uncle, state, wages, easy, hopeless, chains.

Using a Pronunciation Key (page 39)

1. journey; 2. county; 3. enough; 4. suppose; 5. autumn; 6. resemble; 7. crate; 8. quarry; 9. afraid; 10. practice; 11. enemy; 12. cedar; 13. prison; 14. lonely.

Using Guide Words (page 40)

act—fin
1. age
2. boy
3. chase
4. county
5. easy
6. face

final—march
1. frame
2. guard
3. journey
4. liked
5. longer
6. man

mare—tongue
1. mother
2. numbers
3. practice
4. reading
5. stories
6. strangers

Choosing Correct Meanings (page 41)
1. 4; 2. 3; 3. 1; 4. 1; 5. 2; 6. 1; 7. 2; 8. 2; 9. 2; 10. 4; 11. 3; 12. 3; 13. 2; 14. 3; 15. 3; 16. 1.

Making an Outline (page 43)

Lamps

I. Fat or oil
- A. Grease
- B. Tallow
- C. Paraffin
- D. Whale oil
- E. Kerosene

II. Gas
- A. Acetylene
- B. Natural gas
- C. Butane
- D. Coal gas
- E. Water gas

III. Electric
- A. Incandescent
- B. Fluorescent
- C. Mercury vapor
- D. Metal halide
- E. Neon

Finding Facts in the Encyclopedia (page 45)
1. 16, quarry; 2. 4, cistern; 3. 10, iron; 4. 18, stoves; 5. 21, weasel; 6. 9, hound; 7. 2, books; 8. 12, lantern; 9. 13, Montaigne; 10. 4, Cyrus.

CREATIVE SKILLS

Creating a Character (page 46)
Responses will vary.

Creating a Picture (page 47)
Responses and pictures will vary.

Connecting Words (page 48)
Responses will vary.

Writing a Journal Sample (page 49)
Responses will vary.

Using Descriptive Words (page 50)
Responses will vary.

Describing Feelings (page 51)
1. contented; 2. amused; 3. sadness; 4. relieved; 5. surprised; 6. lonely; 7. proud; 8. angry; 9. excited; 10. ashamed.

Explaining Feelings (page 53)
Responses will vary.